FOR THE LOVE OF

Christmas

REBECCA & LAURA BELLISTON

FOR THE LOVE OF

Christmas

ADVANCED INTERMEDIATE PIANO ARRANGEMENTS

Angels We Have Heard on High 21

Hark! The Herald Medley 8

Noel Medley 18

O Come, O Come, Emmanuel 13

Oh, Come, All Ye Faithful 1

OH, COME, ALL YE FAITHFUL

Piano Duet (1P/4H)

Traditional
arranged by Rebecca & Laura Belliston

HARK! THE HERALD MEDLEY

Piano Solo

"Hark! The Herald Angels Sing" and "What Child is This?"

Felix Mendelssohn and Traditional
arranged by Rebecca Belliston

O COME, O COME EMMANUEL

Piano Solo

Traditional
arranged by Rebecca Belliston

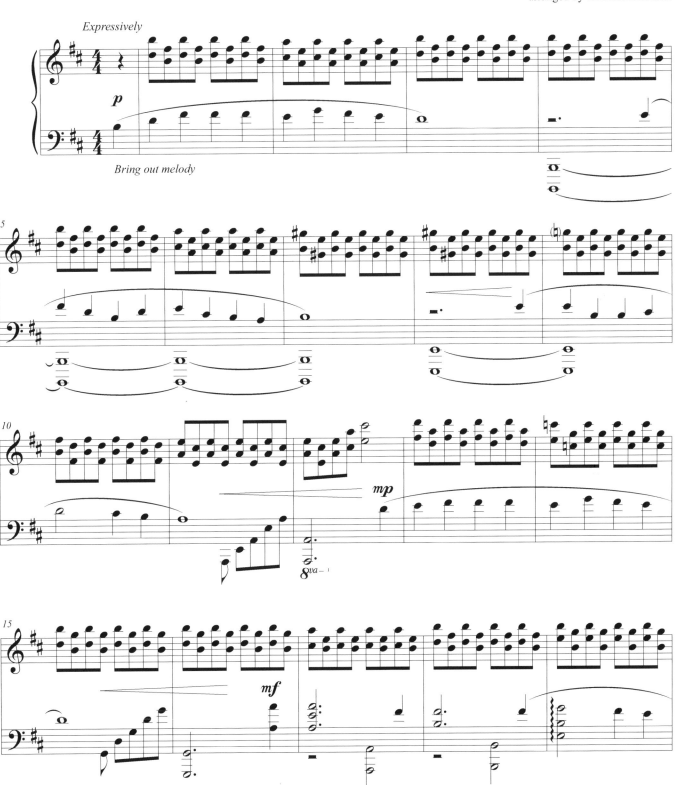

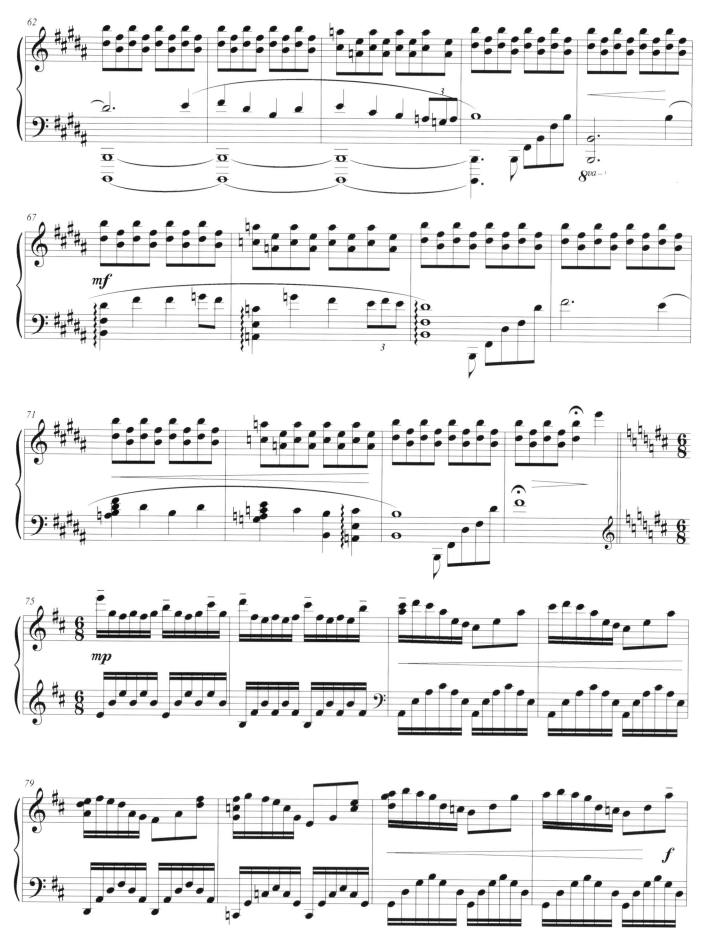

NOEL MEDLEY

Piano Solo

"The First Noel" and "Away In a Manger"

Traditional
Arranged by Rebecca Belliston

ANGELS WE HAVE HEARD ON HIGH

Piano Solo

Arranged by Laura Belliston

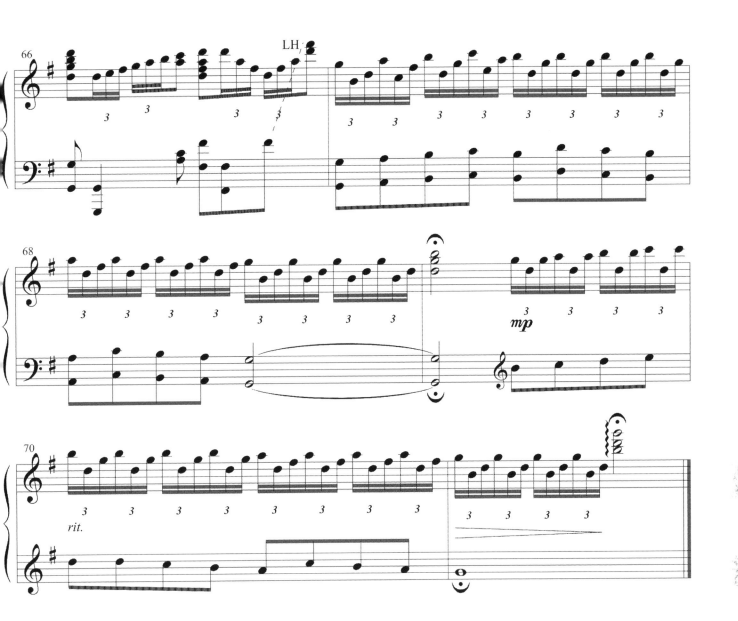

ABOUT THE COMPOSERS

Rebecca and Laura Belliston are a mother/daughter duo from Michigan.
They both love playing and composing for piano,
vocal, and guitar. Rebecca has composed and arranged over sixty
religious and contemporary-classical songs, including
the bestselling choral work, "For There's a Savior Born."
In addition, Rebecca writes romantic suspense novels.
Laura loves to perform and has sung in different venues around
Michigan and Utah. She is currently a student at Brigham Young University
.

CONNECT :
Website: www.rebeccabelliston.com
Facebook: @rebeccalundbelliston
Instagram: @rebeccabelliston
YouTube: @rebeccabelliston
YouTube: @laurabelliston
Soundcloud: @laura-belliston
Spotify: @rebeccabelliston

REBECCA BELLISTON

Original Compositions & Arrangements | Complete listing at rebeccabelliston.com

hymns / religious

A Poor Wayfaring Man of Grief — Piano Solo
Abide With Me; 'Tis Eventide — Piano Solo | Violin Solo
Come, and Be With Me — SATB
Come Unto Jesus — SATB Hymn
The Commandments — Children's Song
Feast Upon His Word — SSAA
For the Love of Hymns —Piano Album
How Great Thou Art — Piano Solo | Vocal Solo & Duet | SATB | Instrumental
I Will Make Weak Things Strong: Ether 12:27 — Men's Vocal Solo
Jesus, the Very Thought of Thee — Piano Solo
Nearer Medley — Vocal Duet
Nearer, Dear Savior, to Thee — Piano Solo | SATB | Violin Solo
Oil For Your Lamps — SSA
Oh, How Lovely Was the Morning —Piano Solo | Piano/Organ Duet | SATB
Souls To Save — Vocal Solo
Still Be My Vision — Vocal Duet | SSA | SATB
We Come Unto Thy House — SATB

christmas

Christmas Handbells for Children — Handbells
Come, Thou Long Expected Jesus — SATB
For the Love of Christmas — Piano Album
For There's a Savior Born — SATB
Hark! The Herald Medley — Piano Solo
Noel: A Christmas Medley — Piano Solo | Vocal Duet | SATB
O Come, O Come Emmanuel — Piano Solo | Vocal Solo
O Holy Night - SATB
Oh, Come, All Ye Faithful — Piano Duet | SATB
Silent Night —Vocal Solo & Duet | SATB | Instrumental
Where Are You Christmas? — Big Note Piano

classical

Andante in A — Piano Solo
Dresden: Fugue in F minor — Piano Duet
Etude in Eb minor — Piano Solo
For the Love of Classical — Piano Album
Fugue in C minor — Piano Solo
Heart of Red, Blood of Blue — Piano Solo Album
Jerusalem: Prelude in C minor — Piano Solo
Prelude in Bb minor — Piano Solo
Sonata in A minor — Piano Solo

contemporary / popular

A Whole New World — Big Note
Cider House Rules — Piano Solo
Greatest Showman Songs — Big Note | Easy Piano | Piano Solo
Look Past — Piano/Vocal/Guitar
My Country, 'Tis of Thee — Piano Solo
Over and Over Again — Piano Solo
Someone You Loved — Piano Solo
Spirit/Run Free — Piano Solo
Sunflower/Spider-Man — Easy Piano

Made in the USA
Monee, IL
16 November 2023

46781433R00020